The WoW Journal

Created for KIDS by KIDS!

Published by Fuzzy Flamingo
www.fuzzyflamingo.co.uk

ISBN 978-1-8380944-6-1:

A CIP catalogue record for this book is available
from the British Library.

Design by: Jen Parker, Fuzzy Flamingo
www.fuzzyflamingo.co.uk

Illustrations by: Molly O'Donoghue, Molly O'Design
www.mollyodonoghue.co.uk

The WOW Journal was invented by
Maddie, age seven,
with the help of Nathan, age five
(and Mummy, age undisclosed).

"We believe that everyone
feels better when we
notice and appreciate the
MASSIVE number of things
that can 'wow' us every day
of our lives."

THE MEANING
OF WOW

wow (interjection) – an expression used to express wonder, amazement, or great pleasure

wow (noun) – an outstanding success; a person or thing that is amazing

wow (transitive verb) – to make someone feel enthusiastic admiration or approval; to 'wow' someone

CONTENTS

WELCOME TO YOUR WOW JOURNAL!

This Journal Belongs To

_____ Zara Zara _____

Shhh! We've got a secret to tell you. Here it comes. Are you ready? Sure? Absolutely sure? 100% sure? Okay, this is it…

Your WOW Journal is magic!

What? That's impossible! How can that be?

Well, here's how it works…

The world is full of wonder.

Everybody knows this. But how often do you really notice it?

Well, your WOW Journal is your invitation to do just that: to notice and note down

the objects, ideas, people and experiences in your life that fill you full of wonder, amazement and deep pleasure.

Things that make you go: "Wow!"

Because – and here's the magic part – the more you write in your WOW Journal, the more you'll notice the many wonderful things that exist in the world and in your life.

Then, as you become more aware of the "wows" in your world, you'll start to appreciate them more. You'll enjoy them more as you come across them, and you'll remember them with greater pleasure, for longer. You'll want to look out for them, look after them, and share them with others.

And finally, by doing all of this, you'll invite more and more and more "wows "into your life. Which will feel pretty awesome!

HOW TO USE YOUR WOW JOURNAL

You don't have to write in your WOW Journal every day. (Unless, of course, you want to!) Writing works best when it's a pleasure, not a chore.

But remember: the more often you write in your WOW Journal, the more you'll notice, appreciate and experience the incredible wonders of your world.

WHAT CAN I WRITE ABOUT?

Hey, it's your journal – it's up to you! But we had some ideas, which we've split into different journal sections:

- Section 1: WOW Lists – People, places, facts, dreams and other things that make you go "Wow!"

- Section 2: WOW Days – Pages for writing about you and your life.

- Section 3: WOW Stories – Inspiration for you to write your own amazing tales.

- Section 4: WOW Doodles – Want a break from writing? Try drawing instead!

You'll find suggestions in each section, to get you started.

So let's get started!

"Let's do this! Get ready to be wowed..."

WOW LISTS

Things that make you go: "Wow!"

You can keep coming back to these lists over and over again to add new items and ideas to them – or simply to re-read what's on them if you're having a bad day, just to make you smile.

"This journal is at the top of our Wow Loves list! We hope you enjoy it, too."

WOW FACTS

Find out and write down some fascinating facts about the world – or even the universe – that make you go "Wow!"

We've started the list off for you...

1. There are more than one trillion galaxies in the observable universe, each of which contains on average more than one hundred billion stars.*

_____

_____

_____

_____

_____

_____

_____

_____

_____

* Professor Brian Cox gave us this fact. He's a famous particle physicist who has presented lots of TV programmes about space, so we're not going to argue with him!

WOW

WOW DREAMS

What are some incredible ambitions that you'd love to achieve? This week, next year, when you grow up, when you're 102! Write them here. And don't forget to dream big – amazingly big!

_____

_____

_____

_____

_____

_____

_____

_____

_____

_____

_____

_____

_____

_____

WOW MENTORS

Mentors are people who inspire you. They may be people you know well, or who you've never met – or even imaginary characters from films or books. Who are yours, and why?

_____

_____

_____

_____

_____

_____

_____

_____

_____

_____

_____

_____

_____

_____

WOW PLACES

Where do you love to spend time – or
where would you love to visit some day? A
special corner in your bedroom; grandma's
house; somewhere fun you visited on holiday;
Disneyland; the moon! Write them here.

_____

_____

_____

_____

_____

_____

_____

_____

_____

_____

_____

_____

_____

_____

_____

WOW LOVES

What do you really, really love about your life? Write down some of your favourite things that always make you smile.

_____
_____
_____
_____
_____
_____
_____
_____
_____
_____
_____
_____
_____
_____
_____
_____

WOW DAYS

Did you know that writing about your day can help you to feel better, no matter what mood you're in?

sad

happy

angry

excited

confused

proud

anxious

loved

You can write about whatever you like here – but we've included some questions, in case you want some inspiration.

"Imagine that the smiley face on each page is a good friend; someone who you can tell anything to, and they'll understand."

Date: _____

How are you feeling today?

Draw your own emoji:

What made you say "Wow!" today?

_____

_____

_____

_____

_____

_____

What else would you like to say today?

_____

_____

_____

_____

_____

Date: _____

How are you feeling today?

Draw your own emoji:

What helped you today?

_____
_____
_____
_____
_____
_____

What else would you like to say today?

_____
_____
_____
_____
_____

Date: _____

How are you feeling today?

Draw your own emoji:

Who was your favourite person today, and why?

_____

_____

_____

_____

_____

_____

What else would you like to say today?

_____

_____

_____

_____

_____

Date: _____

How are you feeling today?

Draw your own emoji:

What superpower would you choose to have, and why?

_____
_____
_____
_____
_____
_____

What else would you like to say today?

_____
_____
_____
_____
_____

Date: _____

How are you feeling today?

Draw your own emoji:

If you had three wishes, what would they be?

_____

_____

_____

_____

_____

_____

What else would you like to say today?

_____

_____

_____

_____

Date: _____

How are you feeling today?

Draw your own emoji:

What made you say "Wow!" today?

_____
_____
_____
_____
_____
_____

What else would you like to say today?

_____
_____
_____
_____
_____

Date: _____

How are you feeling today?

Draw your own emoji:

What could you not live without, and why?

_____
_____
_____
_____
_____
_____

What else would you like to say today?

_____
_____
_____
_____
_____

Date: _____

How are you feeling today?

Draw your own emoji: ⬤

If you could teleport, where would you go?

_____

_____

_____

_____

_____

_____

What else would you like to say today?

_____

_____

_____

_____

_____

Date: _____

How are you feeling today?

Draw your own emoji:

What would you love to do tomorrow?

_____
_____
_____
_____
_____
_____

What else would you like to say today?

_____
_____
_____
_____
_____

Date: _____

How are you feeling today?

Draw your own emoji:

What is your favourite thing to do outdoors, and why?

_____

_____

_____

_____

_____

_____

What else would you like to say today?

_____

_____

_____

_____

Date: _____

How are you feeling today?

Draw your own emoji:

What made you say "Wow!" today?

_____

_____

_____

_____

_____

_____

What else would you like to say today?

_____

_____

_____

_____

_____

Date: _____

How are you feeling today?

Draw your own emoji:

What would you love to be really good at?

_____
_____
_____
_____
_____
_____

What else would you like to say today?

_____
_____
_____
_____
_____

Date: _____

How are you feeling today?

Draw your own emoji:

What do you most like about yourself?

_____

_____

_____

_____

_____

_____

What else would you like to say today?

_____

_____

_____

_____

_____

Date: _____

How are you feeling today?

Draw your own emoji:

Who do you love to spend time with, and why?

_____
_____
_____
_____
_____
_____

What else would you like to say today?

_____
_____
_____
_____
_____

Date: _____

How are you feeling today?

Draw your own emoji:

What is your favourite thing in your bedroom, and why?

_____
_____
_____
_____
_____
_____

What else would you like to say today?

_____
_____
_____
_____
_____

Date: _____

How are you feeling today?

Draw your own emoji:

What made you say "Wow!" today?

_____
_____
_____
_____
_____
_____

What else would you like to say today?

_____
_____
_____
_____
_____

Date: _____

How are you feeling today?

Draw your own emoji:

What would you love to do for your next birthday?

_____
_____
_____
_____
_____
_____

What else would you like to say today?

_____
_____
_____
_____

Date: _____

How are you feeling today?

Draw your own emoji:

What is a nice thing someone said to you recently?

_____

_____

_____

_____

_____

_____

What else would you like to say today?

_____

_____

_____

_____

_____

Date: _____

How are you feeling today?

Draw your own emoji:

Who would you love to meet, and why?

_____
_____
_____
_____
_____
_____

What else would you like to say today?

_____
_____
_____
_____
_____

Date: _____

How are you feeling today?

Draw your own emoji:

What is your favourite animal, and why?

_____

_____

_____

_____

_____

_____

What else would you like to say today?

_____

_____

_____

_____

_____

Date: _____

How are you feeling today?

Draw your own emoji:

What made you say "Wow!" today?

_____
_____
_____
_____
_____
_____

What else would you like to say today?

_____
_____
_____
_____
_____

Date: _____

How are you feeling today?

Draw your own emoji:

How have you helped someone recently?

_____
_____
_____
_____
_____
_____

What else would you like to say today?

_____
_____
_____
_____
_____

Date: _____

How are you feeling today?

Draw your own emoji:

What do you think cats think about?

_____
_____
_____
_____
_____
_____

What else would you like to say today?

_____
_____
_____
_____
_____

Date: _____

How are you feeling today?

Draw your own emoji:

What would you love to do when you're an adult?

_____
_____
_____
_____
_____
_____

What else would you like to say today?

_____
_____
_____
_____
_____

Date: _____

How are you feeling today?

Draw your own emoji:

Who is your favourite fictional character, and why?

_____

_____

_____

_____

_____

_____

What else would you like to say today?

_____

_____

_____

_____

_____

Date: _____

How are you feeling today?

Draw your own emoji:

What made you say "Wow!" today?

_____
_____
_____
_____
_____
_____

What else would you like to say today?

_____
_____
_____
_____
_____

Date: _____

How are you feeling today?

Draw your own emoji:

If your toes could talk, what would they say?

What else would you like to say today?

Date: _____

How are you feeling today?

Draw your own emoji:

What would be an amazing adventure?

_____
_____
_____
_____
_____
_____

What else would you like to say today?

_____
_____
_____
_____
_____

Date: _____

How are you feeling today?

Draw your own emoji:

What is a really happy memory?

_____
_____
_____
_____
_____
_____

What else would you like to say today?

_____
_____
_____
_____
_____

Date: _____

How are you feeling today?

Draw your own emoji:

What is your favourite emotion, and why?

_____

_____

_____

_____

_____

_____

What else would you like to say today?

_____

_____

_____

_____

_____

Date: _____

How are you feeling today?

Draw your own emoji:

What made you say "Wow!" today?

_____

_____

_____

_____

_____

_____

What else would you like to say today?

_____

_____

_____

_____

_____

Date: _____

How are you feeling today?

Draw your own emoji:

What would you like to try for the first time?

_____
_____
_____
_____
_____
_____

What else would you like to say today?

_____
_____
_____
_____
_____

Date: _____

How are you feeling today?

Draw your own emoji:

If you were invisible for a day, what would you do?

_____
_____
_____
_____
_____
_____

What else would you like to say today?

_____
_____
_____
_____

Date: _____

How are you feeling today?

Draw your own emoji:

What makes you amazingly happy?

_____
_____
_____
_____
_____
_____

What else would you like to say today?

_____
_____
_____
_____
_____

Date: _____

How are you feeling today?

Draw your own emoji:

What is your favourite book, and why?

What else would you like to say today?

Date: _____

How are you feeling today?

Draw your own emoji:

What made you say "Wow!" today?

_____

_____

_____

_____

_____

_____

What else would you like to say today?

_____

_____

_____

_____

_____

Date: _____

How are you feeling today?

Draw your own emoji:

If you could go anywhere right now, where would it be?

_____
_____
_____
_____
_____
_____

What else would you like to say today?

_____
_____
_____
_____
_____

Date: _____

How are you feeling today?

Draw your own emoji:

What makes you feel good about yourself?

What else would you like to say today?

Date: _____

How are you feeling today?

Draw your own emoji:

What do you think is the best thing about being a kid?

_____
_____
_____
_____
_____
_____

What else would you like to say today?

_____
_____
_____
_____
_____

Date: _____

How are you feeling today?

Draw your own emoji:

What was the favourite part of your day?

_____
_____
_____
_____
_____
_____

What else would you like to say today?

_____
_____
_____
_____
_____

Date: _____

How are you feeling today?

Draw your own emoji:

What made you say "Wow!" today?

_____
_____
_____
_____
_____
_____

What else would you like to say today?

_____
_____
_____
_____
_____

Date: _____

How are you feeling today?

Draw your own emoji:

What do you think other people like about you?

_____
_____
_____
_____
_____
_____

What else would you like to say today?

_____
_____
_____
_____
_____

Date: _____

How are you feeling today?

Draw your own emoji:

What would be an amazing surprise?

_____

_____

_____

_____

_____

_____

What else would you like to say today?

_____

_____

_____

_____

_____

Date: _____

How are you feeling today?

Draw your own emoji:

What did you find interesting today?

_____
_____
_____
_____
_____
_____

What else would you like to say today?

_____
_____
_____
_____
_____

Date: _____

How are you feeling today?

Draw your own emoji:

What could you never have enough of, and why?

_____
_____
_____
_____
_____
_____

What else would you like to say today?

_____
_____
_____
_____
_____

Date: _____

How are you feeling today?

Draw your own emoji:

What made you say "Wow!" today?

_____
_____
_____
_____
_____
_____

What else would you like to say today?

_____
_____
_____
_____
_____

Date: _____

How are you feeling today?

Draw your own emoji:

What makes you glad to be alive?

_____
_____
_____
_____
_____
_____

What else would you like to say today?

_____
_____
_____
_____
_____

Date: _____

How are you feeling today?

Draw your own emoji:

If you could wish for anything, what would it be?

_____
_____
_____
_____
_____
_____

What else would you like to say today?

_____
_____
_____
_____
_____

Date: _____

How are you feeling today?

Draw your own emoji:

What was the best thing that happened today?

_____

_____

_____

_____

_____

_____

What else would you like to say today?

_____

_____

_____

_____

Date: _____

How are you feeling today?

Draw your own emoji:

What do you like about your friends?

What else would you like to say today?

Date: _____

How are you feeling today?

Draw your own emoji:

What made you say "Wow!" today?

_____
_____
_____
_____
_____
_____

What else would you like to say today?

_____
_____
_____
_____
_____

Date: _____

How are you feeling today?

Draw your own emoji:

Who would you love to meet, and why?

_____
_____
_____
_____
_____
_____

What else would you like to say today?

_____
_____
_____
_____
_____

Date: _____

How are you feeling today?

Draw your own emoji:

What's your favourite game, and why?

_____
_____
_____
_____
_____
_____

What else would you like to say today?

_____
_____
_____
_____
_____

Date: _____

How are you feeling today?

Draw your own emoji:

What would be a nice thing to say to someone you know?

_____

_____

_____

_____

_____

_____

What else would you like to say today?

_____

_____

_____

_____

_____

Date: _____

How are you feeling today?

Draw your own emoji:

If you could have anything in the world, what would it be?

_____

_____

_____

_____

_____

_____

What else would you like to say today?

_____

_____

_____

_____

_____

Date: _____

How are you feeling today?

Draw your own emoji:

What made you say "Wow!" today?

_____
_____
_____
_____
_____
_____

What else would you like to say today?

_____
_____
_____
_____
_____

Date: _____

How are you feeling today?

Draw your own emoji:

What always makes you feel happy?

_____

_____

_____

_____

_____

_____

What else would you like to say today?

_____

_____

_____

_____

_____

Date: _____

How are you feeling today?

Draw your own emoji:

If you could time-travel, when would you go to, and why?

What else would you like to say today?

Date: _____

How are you feeling today?

Draw your own emoji:

Who did you like spending time with today?

_____

_____

_____

_____

_____

_____

What else would you like to say today?

_____

_____

_____

_____

_____

Date: _____

How are you feeling today?

Draw your own emoji:

What's your favourite possession, and why?

_____

_____

_____

_____

_____

_____

What else would you like to say today?

_____

_____

_____

_____

_____

Date: _____

How are you feeling today?

Draw your own emoji:

What made you say "Wow!" today?

What else would you like to say today?

Date: _____

How are you feeling today?

Draw your own emoji:

What makes you feel proud today?

_____
_____
_____
_____
_____
_____

What else would you like to say today?

_____
_____
_____
_____
_____

Date: _____

How are you feeling today?

Draw your own emoji:

If you could read minds, whose would you read, and why?

_____

_____

_____

_____

_____

_____

What else would you like to say today?

_____

_____

_____

_____

_____

Date: _____

How are you feeling today?

Draw your own emoji:

What is your favourite smell, and what is it like?

_____
_____
_____
_____
_____
_____

What else would you like to say today?

_____
_____
_____
_____
_____

Date: _____

How are you feeling today?

Draw your own emoji:

What are you glad to have in your life?

_____
_____
_____
_____
_____
_____

What else would you like to say today?

_____
_____
_____
_____
_____

Date: _____

How are you feeling today?

Draw your own emoji: ⬤

What made you say "Wow!" today?

_____
_____
_____
_____
_____
_____

What else would you like to say today?

_____
_____
_____
_____
_____

Date: _____

How are you feeling today?

Draw your own emoji:

What makes you laugh?

_____
_____
_____
_____
_____
_____

What else would you like to say today?

_____
_____
_____
_____
_____

Date: _____

How are you feeling today?

Draw your own emoji:

Where would you like to go on holiday, and why?

_____

_____

_____

_____

_____

_____

What else would you like to say today?

_____

_____

_____

_____

_____

Date: _____

How are you feeling today?

Draw your own emoji:

What would make a great booby trap?

_____
_____
_____
_____
_____
_____

What else would you like to say today?

_____
_____
_____
_____
_____

Date: _____

How are you feeling today?

Draw your own emoji:

What's your favourite food, and why?

What else would you like to say today?

Date: _____

How are you feeling today?

Draw your own emoji:

What made you say "Wow!" today?

_____
_____
_____
_____
_____
_____

What else would you like to say today?

_____
_____
_____
_____
_____

Date: _____

How are you feeling today?

Draw your own emoji:

What would you like to happen today?

_____

_____

_____

_____

_____

_____

What else would you like to say today?

_____

_____

_____

_____

_____

Date: _____

How are you feeling today?

Draw your own emoji:

If you met Santa, what would you say to him?

_____
_____
_____
_____
_____
_____

What else would you like to say today?

_____
_____
_____
_____
_____

Date: _____

How are you feeling today?

Draw your own emoji:

Who is your favourite superhero, and why?

_____

_____

_____

_____

_____

_____

What else would you like to say today?

_____

_____

_____

_____

_____

Date: _____

How are you feeling today?

Draw your own emoji:

What do you like about yourself?

_____

_____

_____

_____

_____

_____

What else would you like to say today?

_____

_____

_____

_____

_____

Date: _____

How are you feeling today?

Draw your own emoji:

What made you say "Wow!" today?

_____
_____
_____
_____
_____
_____

What else would you like to say today?

_____
_____
_____
_____
_____

Date: _____

How are you feeling today?

Draw your own emoji:

If your family were animals, what would they be?

_____
_____
_____
_____
_____
_____

What else would you like to say today?

_____
_____
_____
_____
_____

Date: _____

How are you feeling today?

Draw your own emoji:

What makes life fun?

_____
_____
_____
_____
_____
_____

What else would you like to say today?

_____
_____
_____
_____
_____

Date: _____

How are you feeling today?

Draw your own emoji:

What would you like to get really good at?

_____
_____
_____
_____
_____
_____

What else would you like to say today?

_____
_____
_____
_____
_____

Date: _____

How are you feeling today?

Draw your own emoji: ( )

What's the coolest thing you've seen today?

_____
_____
_____
_____
_____
_____

What else would you like to say today?

_____
_____
_____
_____
_____

Date: _____

How are you feeling today?

Draw your own emoji:

What made you say "Wow!" today?

_____
_____
_____
_____
_____
_____

What else would you like to say today?

_____
_____
_____
_____
_____

Date: _____

How are you feeling today?

Draw your own emoji:

If you could taste colours, what would some of their flavours be?

_____
_____
_____
_____
_____
_____

What else would you like to say today?

_____
_____
_____
_____
_____

Date: _____

How are you feeling today?

Draw your own emoji:

What would you like to do more often?

_____
_____
_____
_____
_____
_____

What else would you like to say today?

_____
_____
_____
_____
_____

Date: _____

How are you feeling today?

Draw your own emoji:

What's your clearest memory of the day?

_____
_____
_____
_____
_____
_____

What else would you like to say today?

_____
_____
_____
_____
_____

Date: _____

How are you feeling today?

Draw your own emoji:

What weather do you love, and why?

_____
_____
_____
_____
_____
_____

What else would you like to say today?

_____
_____
_____
_____
_____

Date: _____

How are you feeling today?

Draw your own emoji:

What made you say "Wow!" today?

_____

_____

_____

_____

_____

_____

What else would you like to say today?

_____

_____

_____

_____

_____

Date: _____

How are you feeling today?

Draw your own emoji:

If you could do anything right now, what would it be?

_____

_____

_____

_____

_____

_____

What else would you like to say today?

_____

_____

_____

_____

_____

Date: _____

How are you feeling today?

Draw your own emoji:

What sounds do you love?

_____

_____

_____

_____

_____

_____

What else would you like to say today?

_____

_____

_____

_____

_____

Date: _____

How are you feeling today?

Draw your own emoji:

What's your favourite thing about journaling?

_____
_____
_____
_____
_____
_____

What else would you like to say today?

_____
_____
_____
_____
_____

Date: _____

How are you feeling today?

Draw your own emoji:

What do you love about your family?

_____

_____

_____

_____

_____

_____

What else would you like to say today?

_____

_____

_____

_____

_____

WOW STORIES

Do you love using your imagination? Here is your space to let it run free, creating tall tales and playing around with words – maybe even inventing some words of your own!

Use some of the opening lines that we created, re-invent tales that you already know, or start your own stories from scratch.

"We love making up words! You'll find some that we invented on one of these pages – what do you think they could mean?"

Stuck for a starting line? Take one of ours...

1. Mrs Horripotimus was the worst woman ever.
2. All the birds stopped singing on the day that the monster came to town.
3. There was once an evil scientist who had an evil experiment in mind.
4. The prince and princess were on a date in Legoland.
5. "Ugh! That smells horrible!" gasped Sir Plop.
6. One stormy night, a vampire bat came flying into our living room.
7. I knew straight away that this was a magical garden.
8. There were two things in his bag: a key, and a tiny person with a square head.
9. In the darkest part of the darkest cave in the Dark Woods, there lived a Gargantuan Rupedoop.
10. She really wished that she hadn't opened the door.

WOW

WOW

Try using our made-up words in a story!

flobulate

smurgle

glimp

pockmunger

blomber

peeble

clickleclackle

sibblylong

bubdub

crudmungle

WOW

_____
_____
_____
_____
_____
_____
_____
_____
_____
_____
_____
_____
_____
_____
_____
_____
_____
_____
_____
_____
_____

wow

wow

WOW DOODLES

It's not all about words! Sometimes you really want to express yourself in other ways.

These pages give you space to draw whatever you want from the weird and wonderful world around you, or from your even more weird and wonderful imagination!

"We've snuck in some of the things that we love to draw – look out for them!"

WOW

SMASHER

Basher

WOW

WOW

super wow

WOW

WOW

SYCH

Wow

wow

If you love your WOW Journal, come and follow us on social media!

[f] www.facebook..com/thewowjournal

[Instagram] www.instagram.com/the_wow_journal

We'd love to be wowed by some examples of your lists, days, stories and doodles. Share them with us using hashtags:

#thewowjournal #wowjournal

See you there x